PETER ILYICH TCHAIKOVS:

ALBUM FOR THE YC

Op.39

Edited by Howard Ferguson

CW00407906

The pieces are printed in Tchaikovsky's original order, which was altered by the publisher Jürgenson, as shown above in brackets, probably in order to simplify page-layout.

THE ASSOCIATED BOARD OF
THE ROYAL SCHOOLS OF MUSIC

INTRODUCTION

PETER ILYICH TCHAIKOVSKY
(1840–1893)

Shortly after Tchaikovsky had completed his 4th Symphony and the opera *Eugene Onegin* he wrote to his publisher Jürgenson on 14/26 February 1878:

> I'd like to try to write a series of easy pieces, *Kinderstücke*. It would be a pleasant relaxation for me, and perhaps profitable for you. What do you think?

One of the results was the *Album for the Young*, Op.39, whose sub-title '24 easy pieces (à la Schumann)' shows that the composer was influenced by Schumann's *Kinderscenen* (Scenes from Childhood), Op.15 and *Album for the Young*, Op.68, published in 1838 and 1848 respectively. Like Schumann, Tchaikovsky had the happy knack of being able to write for young people without writing down to them; and in so doing he produced what John Warrack has aptly described as this set of 'charming and sometimes touching trifles', which ranges (as do the Schumann pieces) from the very easy (for example, No.12) to the fairly difficult (No.4).

The work was first published by Jürgenson in 1878; but the present text is taken from Tchaikovsky's *Oeuvres complètes pour le piano, Vol.IV: nouvelle édition revue et corrigé par l'auteur*; Jürgenson, Moscow 1893. As noted on page 1, however, the pieces are printed in their original order, which is much more logical than Jürgenson's. The fingering throughout is editorial. Editorial slurs, ties and 'hairpin' *cresc.* and *dim.* signs are crossed with a small vertical stroke, while other editorial additions are printed either within square brackets or in small type. Very occasionally the distribution of notes on the two staves has been altered, when this might make them easier to read.

My thanks are due to the Provost and Fellows of King's College, Cambridge, for allowing access to their copy of the source, and for giving permission for it to be used in establishing the present text.

HOWARD FERGUSON
Cambridge 1981

ALBUM POUR ENFANTS
ALBUM FOR THE YOUNG

Prière du matin - Morning prayer

TCHAIKOVSKY, Op.39
Feb.-Oct.1878

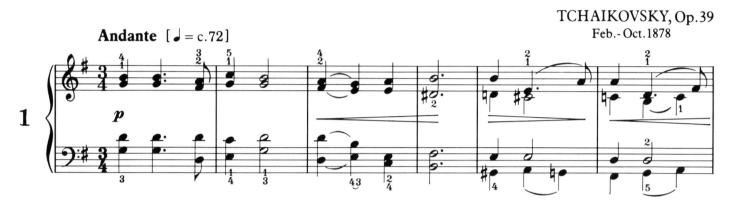

AB 1767

Le matin en hiver - Winter morning

Maman - Mamma

Le petit cavalier - The hobby-horse

1) Bb. 41 & 45, l.h. upper note 2: A in source, not B; but probably a slip (see bb. 1 & 5).

8

Marche des soldats de bois - March of the wooden soldiers

La nouvelle poupée - The new doll

La poupée malade - The sick doll

Enterrement de la poupée - The doll's funeral

Valse - Waltz

Polka - Polka

Mazurka - Mazurka

Chanson russe - Russian song†

12

† Tchaikovsky used a shorter setting of the same tune as No.2 of his *50 Russian Folksongs* for Piano Duet (c.1869), where it has the odd title of 'My little head, my tiny little head'. Note that it is in 3-bar phrases until the last six bars, which consist of three 2-bar phrases.

Le paysan prélude - The peasant's prelude†

13

† The peasant is trying-out his accordion.

Chanson populaire - Folksong

(Kamarinskaya)

Chanson italienne - Italian song

Mélodie antique française - Old French song

Chanson allemande - German song

1) B. 20, l.h. 2nd crotchet: the source adds an F above the D; but this was probably an uncorrected misprint (see bb. 3, 7, etc.).

Chanson napolitaine - Neapolitan song

Conte de la vieille bonne - The old nurse's tale

La sorcière - The witch

(Baba Yaga)†

† The witch Baba Yaga lived in a hut that had chicken's feet; it is portrayed in one of Mussorgsky's *Pictures from an Exhibition*.

Douce rêverie - Daydream

Chant de l'alouette - Song of the lark

A l'église - In church

L'orgue de barberie - The barrel-organ†

† *Not* the piano-barrel-organ heard in Victorian streets, but the wheezy pipe-and-wind variety imitated by Stravinsky in *Petrushka*, scene 1, figure 22.